7 PATHS
to Healing Your Relationship

THE
GUIDING
JOURNAL

ROCHELLE L. COOK
MA., CHT.

Forward by
Michael Glock Ph.D

For permission requests, write to the publisher, addressed "Attention: Permissions Coordinator," at the address below.
Bloom Factor Press
4115 Glencoe Avenue, Suite 105
Marina del Rey, CA 90292
www.bloomfactorpress.com

Ordering Information:
Quantity sales. Special expanded wholesale availability is available on quantity purchases by corporations, associations, and others. For details, contact the publisher CreateSpace >>> www.createspace.com/pub/l/createspacedirect.do or order it through one of the regular wholesalers, e.g., Ingram.

ISBN-10: 0-9891931-4-4
ISBN-13: 978-0-9891931-4-6

Library of Congress In-Publication Data
Cook MA., ChT. Rochelle L.
7 Paths to Healing Your Relationship – The Guiding Journal
1. Spirituality 2. Psychology 3 Self Help

Project, cover and book design directed by Michael Glock Ph.D.
Typesetting by Ramesh Kumar
Interior typeset in Sabon (body) & Oswald (Chapter)
Front/back cover painting by © Gregg Chadwick Used by permission: May 10 2016
www.greggchadwick.com/
Printed in the United States of America
First printing – September 2016

20 19 18 17 16 15 14 13 12 11 10 9 8 7 6 5 4 3 2 1

DEDICATION DATE:

....

I ....

dedicate this journal work to

....

....

....

....

....

....

....

....

....

....

....

....

....

....

....

....

....

N.B. Dedicate this page to yourself or to a significant person. Show them this journal a few years after you have filled it up and tell them your story.

Disclaimer

This Guiding Journal is not intended as a substitute for the medical advice of physicians or mental license professionals. The reader should regularly consult a physician in matters relating to his/her health, mental health and particularly with respect to any psychological or physical symptoms that may require diagnosis or medical attention.

CONTENTS

P.S. Add your own page numbers related to the exercises you have worked on when working through the Wisdom Triangle Workbook. Do this and then reference these notes in the future. In 2, 4 or 9 years you will be astonished to see what happened.

EARLY ACLAIM FOR

The Soul's Coach - 7 Paths To Healing Your Relationship

Wow! What can I say other than Rochelle is one of the most amazingly authentic people on the planet. Even when walking through some of my darkest moments I never felt judgment or discomfort when I am doing work with her. I have seen a lot of people for therapy and other inner work-they all pale in comparison to the work that Rochelle naturally does. I HIGHLY recommend Rochelle if you have blocks or if you suffer from anything mentally, spiritually or physically, as she is a true miracle worker! I will always utilize her services as she makes me feel beyond good during and after our sessions!!

Amy F. Seattle, WA

Rochelle is an inspiring and intelligent person. She has helped me so quickly with so many deep rooted issues that I feel like I have been stuck with for so long. I cannot thank her enough for helping me start a new journey. Her technique works, and it is a wonderful to be in her company.

I have never tried hypnotherapy before, but I am so grateful to have found Rochelle because I have realized that is she gives so much more. She is an incredible spiritual guide, filled with light and love.

India W. Venice, CA

I strongly recommend Rochelle as a therapist. I went in to see Rochelle based on a good recommendation by a friend because I was dealing with difficult family relationships stemming from the recent passing of a parent. I gained so much from her incredibly accurate and helpful analysis, and she provides a number of powerful visualization and spiritual exercises that helped me gain a better and healthier perception of others and myself. I feel as though a great weight has been lifted off my shoulders and I look forward to continued work with such a great professional.

Tim C. Venice, CA

Rochelle gets five stars because she is DEDICATED TO HELPING OTHERS & she has the SKILL SET TO DO IT. Her experience, training, intuitive nature & compassion helped me connect with my past and guided me through a TRANSFORMATIONAL PROCESS that gave me understanding and freedom. I HIGHLY RECOMMEND you to meet with Rochelle and experience this for yourself. Thank you Rochelle for all you have given me so far.

Maxine W. Los Angeles, CA

Rochelle is the real deal! She is extremely articulate, smart, honest and warm. She gained my trust almost instantaneously, she is incredible. Ask for what you want and you shall receive with this miracle worker. She has changed my life and I've only had 4 sessions.

Annie P. Manhattan, NY

Transformational is an apt description of the experience derived from Rochelle's expertise. With her intuitive, intelligent and enthusiastic approach to hypnosis, she brought an astonishing amount of clarity and peace in our sessions. She is a warm, spiritual and sensitive person and a brilliant communicator. I immediately felt comfortable with her and confident in her abilities. The process is fascinating, enjoyable and very effective. I highly recommend Rochelle to anyone grappling with the many issues she is dedicated to healing.

Michele P. Beverly Hills, CA

FORWARD

A JOURNALING MIND - THRIVES

Discover the Self

For many, our constructed post-modern world has hindered, perhaps even extinguished the deep and profoundly powerful awareness of our own interiority. This inner realm when revealed and integrated offers a fundamental gateway to a very different life. You will enhance thinking, expand your imagination, dream more, have insights, become more intuitive and live a more symbolic life.

If you have recently attended a workshop, retreat, seminar or program or you have recently read *The Soul's Coach – 7 Paths to Healing Relationship* by Rochelle L. Cook you may have heard the suggestion – work-the-workbook and start a journal.

Heed the suggestions and you will gain clarity over your life, empower yourself and begin shifting into the paths your life was meant to travel.

The precise observation of your daily accomplishments is psychologically meaningful and will lead to your own Mind – Thriving. This is what will happen when you work the workbook and journal.

The internal witnessing of your own stories and dreams is a royal road to unconcealing unconscious attitudes and patterns that are *for now* holding you back.

THE SUBCONSCIOUS RULES YOUR LIFE!

Following along with the suggestions in this workbook and gratitude journaling is a Depth Psychological process. The modern field of Depth Psychology originated in the work of Carl G. Jung and Sigmund Freud, two leading visionaries who called attention to the importance of what lies hidden and below the surface of conscious awareness.

This dimension of psychic reality is revealed in the movies we watch, in great literature, the expressive arts of different cultures, dreams, and in the collective symptoms suffered by individuals and cultures. The central concept at the core of depth psychology is to bring unconsciousness to consciousness. This is the secret underlying – wisdom, knowing thyself. The importance of making meaning of the images and metaphors in personal and cultural expression is a threshold we must all cross and master in order to gain soulful wisdom. The exquisite interplay between the aesthetics of the natural world and the human experience, are critical – for soul making.

Understanding your future with greater clarity, foresight, and clarity requires imagination. Descending into and returning from the dreamy and mythic underworld that underpins the world of everyday reality releases the imaginative power that produces fresh thinking and yes – foresight. This is the task of managing your reality by using the workbook and of journaling – as personal psychoanalysis and the function of depth psychology. It is a healing journey, because one must confront personal and collective shadows in order to discover the Self.

CHANGE YOUR CONSCIOUSNESS ABOUT ANYTHING?

Practice the art of Gratitude! You have heard it before, "be thankful for what you do have!" One of the easiest ways to change negative thinking is to state how grateful you are. When you allow yourself to think and live daily in a positive frame – it becomes what you attract. When you vibrate at a higher frequency some of your unconscious material becomes known to consciousness and this elevates your consciousness to a new level.

HAVE YOU EVER ALLOWED THE PART OF YOU THAT HURTS SPEAK?

The unconscious mind is highly skilled when it comes to misunderstanding and harboring judgments of actions and negative experiences from the past. These dark and often unresolved and unknown issues have a way of surfacing from the depths and becoming monstrous. Listening to and allowing these dark voices to speak, frees the unconscious from being gripped, often – by the fear. By revealing, working and learning to forgive this previously unknown unconscious material, you offer like a host a table for your guest, this form of hospitality produces reconciliation and allows the healing process to begin.

WRITING DOWN DAILY GRATITUDE'S, IS REALLY A FORM OF SAYING GRACE.

Use the journal to answer questions and jot ideas down, tend an image that has revealed itself in a moment of day or night dreaming. Draw, sketch, and write anything that catches your attention. Importantly, do not judge the material, nor attempt at interpreting any dreams you may have. Tend only to the images in the dreams, feel it in your body, stay true to the image. Amplify the image with notes and work at keeping the image alive in your minds eye during the day in order to intensify the message coming through. These amplifications will lead to the way within.

Notice any synchronicities you encounter while out and about. Taking note of these, will reveal to you, your own mind working in concordance with the world. Writing your gratitude's daily will ignite the creativity in your soul. Add sketches or images to your gratitude's, this will deepen your vision for the future and free your self-expression.

During the day take breaks, go for a walk, meditate on every step, notice the world around you and pick up any interesting object that enters your path of consciousness. Draw it; place the flower you picked into your journal, draw spirals, or the shell from the beach. Draw the directions of the compass.

Write that you are grateful for: life, love, breathe, friends, family son, daughter, husband, wife, dog, cat, horse, clouds, trees, job, wisdom…

There are 10,000 reasons to have gratitude and journal. It is indeed a heroic journey. The journal will help you to remember just how extraordinary your own hand-made life is. You will stimulate your own creativity, while reflecting on material that will guide you forward.

"Is it not true… that the river has many voices… Does it not have the voice of a King, and of a warrior, and of a bull, and of a night bird, and of a woman giving birth, and of a sighing man, and a thousand other voices?" (Hesse, 2003, p. 95)[1]

The workbook and your journal is your private river, leading you towards, the way within. Writing down what happens to you on a daily basis means that nothing will be forgotten. Feelings, thoughts and the memories of incidents and events begin to fade as time goes on. By recording them, you witness your own gratifying journey.

PROOF AND TRUTH!

What is truth? Truth is what you hear when you are silent. The authentic Self knows nothing else. The truth is what you feel in the core of your being. Whenever you feel upset ask yourself: "Is it true?" "Is it true that I need to eat that bite of chocolate cake. Is it true that I need someone else to love me?"

USE THE JOURNAL TO DOCUMENT - EVIDENCE.

Write down, all the wonderful things you have done in your life. E.G. I have worked and provided for my family. I have changed careers. I have enjoyed kind and loving relationships. The idea is to remind our subconscious mind on how much you have done in your life! Allow your subconscious to see the proof.

Your journal will nourish, and enhance your writing and help you clarify your beliefs and spiritual directions. Use the journal to set goals and motivate yourself through setbacks and despair, joy and sadness. Dark and difficult times are just as great an opportunity to build the strength you need to become wise. The journal will also help you to stay organized and remember things to do. Journaling will soon become a great friend. You will discover how your own mind works and how you truly feel about a situation at home, at work or in relationship with another.

---

1 Hesse, H. (2003) *Siddharta*. Translated by Joachim Neugroschel, New York, Penguin Classics Deluxe Edition.

AFFIRMATIONS

We are believers of writing affirmations, they do change reality! "I am grateful that I made self honoring choices to nourish my mind and body so that I am now able to live a wonderful, fulfilled, peaceful life." Affirmations entrench themselves into the subconscious mind. Writing these words on paper creates an ideomotor response and cements these beliefs into the unconscious.

REALITY JOURNALING

Paint yourself a picture of what is happening right here and now. Write in detail using the five senses. What do you see? How does it smell? What does it taste like? What can you smell? How does it feel? What is your story of gratefulness? The mind believes what you tell it. In order to change your mind you must change your reality. Allow this process to be fun, be creative and witness a wonderful journey unfold. By acknowledging the positive in your life as gratitude you mitigate the negative and destructive self-talk that has in fact, created the world you currently inhabit. Create a new world for yourself by creating a new reality. This exercise works for anything you desire in your life ranging from buying a house to relieving depression.

Journaling will lead to the discovery of the most intimate elements of your personality, the Self. "This progression from the unconscious to the conscious and from the ego to the self" (Ellenberger, 1970, p. 672)[2] Carl Jung named the *individuation process*.

GIVING YOURSELF PERMISSION AND SET YOUR INTENTIONS.

Have you ever given yourself permission to recognize and release the judgments you have held onto from the past? Give yourself permission to honor your intention to become free.

"I give myself permission to let go of the misbelief that food is my best friend and coping mechanism. My intention is to honor and nourish the temple in which I live, my physical body."

---

2 Ellenberger, H. F. (1970). *The discovery of the unconscious: The history and evolution of dynamic psychiatry*. New York: Basic Books.

"I give myself permission to let go of my self sabotaging habits and hold onto my new healthy ones. My intention is to embrace loving and honoring myself. My intention is to be the very best me."

The accountability of a journal forces you to witness the world with greater fidelity, you will either gather insight into your life or you will more clearly see the life that's been in front of you all along.

We are now living a psychological life; it is the next evolutionary development for all of us. Freshly alive in all phenomena, peoples and systems of our world.

Play your part - explore living mythically and start journaling today.

Cheers

Introduction

7 Paths to Healing your Relationship
The Guiding Journal

By Rochelle L. Cook MA., ChT.

"You can search throughout the entire universe for someone who is more deserving of your love and affection than you are yourself, and that person is not to be found anywhere. You yourself, as much as anybody in the entire universe deserves your love and affection." Buddha

---

Before you use this journal please read the book, *The Soul's Coach 7 Paths to Healing Your Relationship*. By reading the book and understanding it's 7 paths you will effectively work the process. Please take your time, Rome wasn't built in a day, be honest with yourself, and allow your heart, spirit and mind to heal.

INSTRUCTIONS:

The journal is recommended to be used in conjunction with the wisdom triangle workbook which comprises of twelve exercises to be worked on over three months.

REMEMBER - WE RECOMMEND YOU ALSO KEEP A GUIDING JOURNAL!

This is the guiding journal that goes hand-in-hand with the workbook, and the book *The Soul's Coach – 7 Paths to healing Relationship.*

Journaling on a daily basis is the most powerful cornerstone and habit you can acquire. If done correctly, you will show up better in every area of your life. Without question, journaling has always been the number one factor to everything I've done, including my husband and daughter, well in my life. This includes the lives of my clients.

By writing in your journal in the morning or evening, you will quickly see the incongruences in your life. Some people write in the morning and the evening, this creates a safe container that allows one to stay on course. You will see clearly what negative thoughts need to be removed and what positive and reframed thoughts should be included in your life. Along with the workbook, journaling is a wonderful and powerful facilitator of self-discovery. Through my own journaling I've come to form my sense of identity and path in life.

You will notice that at the end of each exercise in this workbook and in the journal I ask you to write what you are forgiving yourself for and what you are grateful for. I do this so that each day you will clearly speak to the universe and thereby change your perception.

Science has proven that the practice of gratitude is a way to overcome several psychological challenges. The benefits are endless, here a few to think about:

- ♦ Gratitude makes you more happy

- ♦ Gratitude strengthens your emotions

- ♦ Gratitude increases spirituality

- ♦ Gratitude makes you healthier

- ♦ Gratitude makes you more optimistic

- ♦ Gratitude lets you live longer

- ♦ Gratitude helps you bounce back from challenges

"Healing is a mystery, a dance between you, this workbook, your counselor, and especially the Great Spirit. So stay open and alert, and tune in so you can hear the guidance from within and without. This is an adventure of a lifetime in body and soul." – Rochelle L. Cook

"The secret of change is to focus all of your energy, not on fighting the old, but on building the new." ~ Socrates

NOW LETS GET TO WORK!

When you use this journal you can allow the quotes to guide your jouranling process or you can simply observe them and allow them to inspire you. Or, just write down how you feel or what you are experiencing at the present moment.

The good life is a process, not a state of being. It is a direction not a destination.
~ Carl Rogers

Knowing your own darkness is the best method for dealing with the darkness's of other people. ~ Carl Jung

Remember: Use this page to doodle, draw or sketch.what you feel or dreamed.

But let there be spaces in your togetherness
and let the winds of the heavens dance between you.
Love one another but make not a bond of love,
let it rather be a moving sea between the shores of your souls.
~ Kahlil Gibran

Remember: What is my proof & truth? What am I grateful for? What do I affirm? What is my intention?

You Can Transform Your Life.

Remember: Use this page to doodle, draw or sketch.what you feel or dreamed.

*"I Am Not What Happened to Me, I Am What I Choose to Become." ~ **C.G. Jung***

Remember: What is my proof & truth? What am I grateful for? What do I affirm? What is my intention?

When you tend to a garden you must uproot the dry weeds to enjoy the beautiful flowers, so to gain emotional wellbeing you must uproot your negative thoughts and false beliefs to enjoy a beautiful life.

Remember: Use this page to doodle, draw or sketch.what you feel or dreamed.

"We are shaped by our thoughts; we become what we think. When the mind is pure, joy follows like a shadow that never leaves." ~ **Buddha**

Remember: What is my proof & truth? What am I grateful for? What do I affirm? What is my intention?

Relationships do not determine who we are. Neither do the matrial things such as cars and nice houses. They are illusions.

Remember: Use this page to doodle, draw or sketch.what you feel or dreamed.

Life is like a seesaw: when we are up we feel as though the world is our oyster, we think we have all the answers, we are full of life and smiles. When we are down we are in the trenches of upset, operating in the lower realms of consciousness, attracting into our lives more of what we don't want. If we were to sit in the middle of the seesaw we would be in the neutral zone, which is our authentic, divine self – intuitive, peaceful, wise, kind and compassionate. Swaying on the seesaw from one side to the other we experience the illusions and projections on both sides, which can be uncomfortable and disorienting. Eventually we learn to return to center. In the center, we find peace.

Remember: What is my proof & truth? What am I grateful for? What do I affirm? What is my intention?

Your past experiences make you stronger. You are able to appreciate the good in the world and contribute to it.

Healing is a journey not a one-time event or destination, healing means living life consciously.

Remember: What is my proof & truth? What am I grateful for? What do I affirm? What is my intention?

*"The secret of change is to focus all of your energy, not on fighting the old, but on building the new." ~ **Socrates***

....

....

....

....

....

....

....

....

....

....

....

....

....

....

....

....

....

....

....

....

....

....

Remember: Use this page to doodle, draw or sketch. what you feel or dreamed.

We believe that our relationships will be as romantic and fantastic as those we see in the movies and on television. When they are not, we think that something is wrong with us. Rests assure, nothing is wrong, you are just living life. Those who remain flexible, respect their boundaries and refuse to judge, will find the peace they search for.

Remember: What is my proof & truth? What am I grateful for? What do I affirm? What is my intention?

Perfection does not exist. It only exists in the Story Book.

....

....

....

....

....

....

....

....

....

....

....

....

....

....

....

....

....

....

....

....

....

Remember: Use this page to doodle, draw or sketch.what you feel or dreamed.

The minute you stop wanting and needing and looking and obsessing, and you take a deep breath and let life come to you in ways that you do not even predict or expect, the sooner you will find what you are looking for, and better.

"The ability to be in the present moment is a major component of mental wellness."
~ Abraham Maslow

....

....

....

....

....

....

....

....

....

....

....

....

....

....

....

....

....

....

....

....

....

Remember: Use this page to doodle, draw or sketch.what you feel or dreamed.

We Don't Have to Be What We Were Taught.

Remember: What is my proof & truth? What am I grateful for? What do I affirm? What is my intention?

We are all souls sharing a human experience. We come into this world – perfect in our imperfection.

....
....
....
....
....
....
....
....
....
....
....
....
....
....
....
....
....
....
....
....
....
....

Remember: Use this page to doodle, draw or sketch.what you feel or dreamed.

"The good life is a process, not a state of being. It is a direction not a destination."
~ Carl Rogers

Remember: What is my proof & truth? What am I grateful for? What do I affirm? What is my intention?

In order to evolve: to learn more compassion, more loving, more peace and harmony, we come in with the purpose to become more whole. The sooner we understand who we are, what our natural talents and gifts are and what our lessons are, the sooner we will find what we are searching for.

Remember: Use this page to doodle, draw or sketch.what you feel or dreamed.

*"The issue is not the issue, but how you relate to the issue is the issue," ~ **Dr. Ronald Hulnick**, **CEO of the University of Santa Monica.***

This being human is a guest house. Every morning a new arrival. ~ **Jellaludin Rumi,**

Remember: Use this page to doodle, draw or sketch.what you feel or dreamed.

"Knowing is the absents of doubt." ~ **Wayne Dyer**

Remember: What is my proof & truth? What am I grateful for? What do I affirm? What is my intention?

Relationships are high spiritual work. As you diligently work on yourself and are true to yourself and your partner, you may realize that everything you've ever wanted is standing right in front of you. It's your own issues and irrational beliefs about relationships that have been blocking your view.

....
....
....
....
....
....
....
....
....
....
....
....
....
....
....
....
....
....
....
....

Remember: Use this page to doodle, draw or sketch.what you feel or dreamed.

"The only person who is educated is the one who has learned how to learn and change".
~ Carl Rogers

Remember: What is my proof & truth? What am I grateful for? What do I affirm? What is my intention?

Each of our stories – our issues and our journeys of healing – is custom made and contains the exact lessons our individual souls need to learn.

Remember: Use this page to doodle, draw or sketch.what you feel or dreamed.

I know I can heal my life. I know I can manifest what it is I want. I know that, "I" am in control of my thoughts.

My thoughts determine how I feel.

....

....

....

....

....

....

....

....

....

....

....

....

....

....

....

....

....

....

....

....

....

....

....

Remember: Use this page to doodle, draw or sketch.what you feel or dreamed.

"Knowing your own darkness is the best method for dealing with the darkness's of other people." ~ Carl Jung

Remember: What is my proof & truth? What am I grateful for? What do I affirm? What is my intention?

You have the freedom to carve out your own life – create and star in your own Story Book.

Remember: Use this page to doodle, draw or sketch.what you feel or dreamed.

"You enter the forest at the darkest point, where there is no path. Where there is a way or path, it is someone else's path. You are not on your own path. If you follow someone else's way, you are not going to realize your potential." **~ Joseph Campbell**

Remember: What is my proof & truth? What am I grateful for? What do I affirm? What is my intention?

Perfection is an inbuilt mechanism for failure. Those who seek the perfect mate, the perfect relationship, end up alone. Nothing is as you have been told it is, or should be. Nothing.

....

....

....

....

....

....

....

....

....

....

....

....

....

....

....

....

....

....

....

....

....

Remember: Use this page to doodle, draw or sketch.what you feel or dreamed.

Seeking perfection lets you off the hook. You say, "If it's not perfect one, I don't want it at all," and you parachute yourself straight out of any possibility of a relationship.

Remember: What is my proof & truth? What am I grateful for? What do I affirm? What is my intention?

Stand tall and believe in what you want. We must live the life of our choice. We can treat others with compassion and respect but that does not mean that we have to give up our own happiness.

Remember: Use this page to doodle, draw or sketch.what you feel or dreamed.

What you think so shall you be, out of the invisible world you will attract. You thoughts are the first step.

"Is it not true... that the river has many voices... Does it not have the voice of a King, and of a warrior, and of a bull, and of a night bird, and of a woman giving birth, and of a sighing man, and a thousand other voices?" ~ **Hermann Hesse**

Remember: Use this page to doodle, draw or sketch.what you feel or dreamed.

In one way or another, at some point in our lives, we all suffer from what I call the Story Book Syndrome. From classical literature to popular media we are told enchanting stories about knights carrying their princesses into the sunset. Such perfection as displayed in the Story Book does not exist and only creates false expectations. No relationship is perfect. Every relationship requires work and this work starts with work on ourselves. We are all worthy and deserving no matter what to be happy and live in peace.

Remember: What is my proof & truth? What am I grateful for? What do I affirm? What is my intention?

"The meeting of two personalities is like the contact of two chemical substances: if there is any reaction, both are transformed." ~ Carl Jung

Remember: Use this page to doodle, draw or sketch.what you feel or dreamed.

What you put your attention on you will continue to manifest into your life.

Remember: What is my proof & truth? What am I grateful for? What do I affirm? What is my intention?

*"People are like stained - glass windows. They sparkle and shine when the sun is out, but when the darkness sets in, their true beauty is revealed only if there is a light from within." ~ **Elisabeth Kubler-Ross***

....
....
....
....
....
....
....
....
....
....
....
....
....
....
....
....
....
....
....
....
....
....

If you put your attention on what has always has been, is what you will continue to manifest, "what it has been," into your life.

*"The meeting of two personalities is like the contact of two chemical substances: if there is any reaction, both are transformed." ~ **Carl Jung***

Remember: Use this page to doodle, draw or sketch.what you feel or dreamed.

Unless we unlock the little door to our subconscious mind and disarm the "soldiers" that guard our soul, we will not be able to realize our full potential.

We can choose to run, hide or give up, or we can admit the falsehood of our mask, understand why and how we created it, and allow ourselves to be human; allow the parts of ourselves we have kept hidden to be revealed, healed and integrated.

Remember: Use this page to doodle, draw or sketch.what you feel or dreamed.

Our own Trojan Horse is the abode of our subconscious mind that envelops our soul.

Stand tall and believe in what you want. We must live the life of our choice. We can treat others with compassion and respect but that does not mean that we have to give up our own happiness.

....

....

....

....

....

....

....

....

....

....

....

....

....

....

....

....

....

....

....

....

....

Remember: Use this page to doodle, draw or sketch.what you feel or dreamed.

Like nature, life cycles through seasons and after winter spring and summer always come. Remain flexible and give up your judgments. They are all good!

Remember: What is my proof & truth? What am I grateful for? What do I affirm? What is my intention?

"As far as we can discern, the sole purpose of human existence is to kindle a light in the darkness of mere being." ~ Carl Jung

Remember: Use this page to doodle, draw or sketch.what you feel or dreamed.

Like seeds that germinate in response to the correct amount of daylight, temperature and rainfall before a plant is ready to emerge, so to experience our spring and to bloom we must make a significant shift in our lives and work mindfully and diligently to create and sustain it.

We create the chaos we live in and have learned to feel comfortable in what we've created. It has become our comfort zone. Today, walk the other way.

Remember: Use this page to doodle, draw or sketch.what you feel or dreamed.

"In all chaos there is a cosmos, in all disorder a secret order." ~ *Carl Jung*

Remember: What is my proof & truth? What am I grateful for? What do I affirm? What is my intention?

Our basic identity is formed in childhood and as adults we are still only grown up children reacting unconsciously and automatically to life's twists and turns. Allow the grown up to take control and live. Be happy and embrace all that is before you.

Remember: Use this page to doodle, draw or sketch.what you feel or dreamed.

Good news, the chaos we unconsciously create becomes our mirror and potent ground for healing and transformation.

Remember: What is my proof & truth? What am I grateful for? What do I affirm? What is my intention?

Understanding the root cause of chaos, you will be surprised and experience an "aha" moment followed by deeper peace.

Remember: Use this page to doodle, draw or sketch.what you feel or dreamed.

"Being entirely honest with oneself is a good exercise." ~ **Sigmund Freud**

Remember: What is my proof & truth? What am I grateful for? What do I affirm? What is my intention?

In chaos is the seed of creativity, in darkness the emergence of the light.

Remember: Use this page to doodle, draw or sketch.what you feel or dreamed.

Each one of us has experienced at some point in our lives being in a pure and safe space. By healing the deep scars that trauma leaves and learning to re-parent the sad, lonely inner child that still lives inside of us, we create a renewed safe space for us to live in. We can stand tall, smile and breath. We can be grateful for what we now have and the lessons we have learned. We are NOT our past, we are our here and now.

Remember: What is my proof & truth? What am I grateful for? What do I affirm? What is my intention?

"Until you make the unconscious conscious, it will direct your life and you will call it fate". ~ **C.G. Jung**

Remember: Use this page to doodle, draw or sketch.what you feel or dreamed.

Our lives are the outcome of our thoughts; when we change our thinking our life will change.

Remember: What is my proof & truth? What am I grateful for? What do I affirm? What is my intention?

*"Nothing in the affairs of men is worthy of great anxiety."~ **Plato***

Remember: Use this page to doodle, draw or sketch. what you feel or dreamed.

Our outer reality is a reflection of our inner reality – whatever is going on "out there" is a mirror that holds the key to our healing.

Remember: What is my proof & truth? What am I grateful for? What do I affirm? What is my intention?

*"A man should not strive to eliminate his complexes but to get into accord with them: they are legitimately what directs his conduct in the world." ~ **Sigmund Freud***

Remember: Use this page to doodle, draw or sketch.what you feel or dreamed.

Healing is a process and is best viewed not as a ladder to climb but as a jigsaw puzzle with pieces falling into place allowing us to see and understand the connections between events in our lives.

Healing is a mystery, a dance between you, your counselor, and especially the Great Spirit. So stay open and alert, and tune in so you can hear the guidance from within and without. This is an adventure of a lifetime in body and soul.

....

....

....

....

....

....

....

....

....

....

....

....

....

....

....

....

....

....

....

....

....

....

....

Remember: Use this page to doodle, draw or sketch.what you feel or dreamed.

*"You are essentially who you create yourself to be and all that occurs in your life is the result of your own making." ~ **Stephen Richards***

Relationships are often compromised because we are obsessed with the past and all the traumatic experiences we have endured, and are convinced our future will be doomed as well. We live in the past with imagined fears about the future that create a false sense of reality and keep us from being present. We are not our past, we are our here and now. What is your new glorious story? We choose what we think.

Remember: Use this page to doodle, draw or sketch.what you feel or dreamed.

You will always see yourself when you look in the mirror. SMILE!

Remember: What is my proof & truth? What am I grateful for? What do I affirm? What is my intention?

There are two kinds of people: those who always take the blame for a problem at the expense of their own wellbeing, they are the doormat types, and those who always point the finger towards the other person in blame, with them it's always someone's else's fault. Whatever your pattern? Take personal responsibility and you gain back your power. "I am upset because I."

....

....

....

....

....

....

....

....

....

....

....

....

....

....

....

....

....

....

....

....

Remember: Use this page to doodle, draw or sketch.what you feel or dreamed.

Sometimes, those of us who don't like to ruffle anyone's feathers, must take the risk and tell our partner, "You know what? What you just did was not okay with me!" At other times keeping yourself in check and taking personal responsibility for your part in the relationship problem is exactly what's called for. Step up, don't be afraid and allow your voice to be heard.

Remember: What is my proof & truth? What am I grateful for? What do I affirm? What is my intention?

Often life forces us to leave our comfort zone in order to grow, this is just how life works!

Remember: Use this page to doodle, draw or sketch.what you feel or dreamed.

You react dramatically, unconsciously, and you may even experience upset– you have just been triggered! Learning to identify your triggers is the key to healing. Triggers are the masters of disguise controlling your destiny. The past is only the past, let go now and live in there glorious here and now.

Remember: What is my proof & truth? What am I grateful for? What do I affirm? What is my intention?

Think of a puppet and the puppeteer that controls the puppet. For as long as you   do not recognize what your triggers are, your past is the puppeteer that controls your next move. STOP … puppet's are not real, YOU ARE IN CHARGE! We are not our past, we are our here and now and what we choose it to be.

Remember: Use this page to doodle, draw or sketch.what you feel or dreamed.

Triggers can spin you out of control and down the rabbit hole you go. More unhealthy thoughts are created in your mind that spiral you further out of control. I AM NOT MY PAST, I am no longer triggered because right here and now my life is fine. I am an adult and I understand that then was then and now is now. My now is perfectly fine and I am grateful for the lessons I have learned and who I've become.

Remember: What is my proof & truth? What am I grateful for? What do I affirm? What is my intention?

Identifying triggers is the first step out of denial. Work to conquer the belief behind the trigger, release the emotional charge you still carry as a result, and get on with your wonderful happy life.

....

....

....

....

....

....

....

....

....

....

....

....

....

....

....

....

....

....

....

....

....

....

Remember: Use this page to doodle, draw or sketch.what you feel or dreamed.

I am what I think.

Remember: What is my proof & truth? What am I grateful for? What do I affirm? What is my intention?

I am powerful, I choose which thoughts "I" want to think and live accordingly.

I am a lucky happy, healthy person!

Until healed, the past will project itself all over the future. But the past is gone, the future is not here yet, and there is no other place and time to live in but here and now.

....
....
....
....
....
....
....
....
....
....
....
....
....
....
....
....
....
....
....
....
....

Remember: Use this page to doodle, draw or sketch.what you feel or dreamed.

Living in the past prevents you from being present to all that you are and can do and can have right now.

Many people see the world through the dark. Those who truly practice the here and now live in the light of freedom.

Remember: Use this page to doodle, draw or sketch.what you feel or dreamed.

Fear gets in the way of everything. If you are like me, I can only imagine how many times you wanted to make a decision of some sort and fear stopped you. STOP IT!

Remember: What is my proof & truth? What am I grateful for? What do I affirm? What is my intention?

"People are just as wonderful as sunsets if you let them be. When I look at a sunset, I don't find myself saying, "Soften the orange a bit on the right hand corner." I don't try to control a sunset. I watch with awe as it unfolds." ~ **Carl R. Rogers, A Way of Being**

Remember: Use this page to doodle, draw or sketch.what you feel or dreamed.

We only dare to engage in anything, relationship, job, travel, when we know the outcome will be pleasurable, profitable and successful. Uncertainty triggers the fear and disappointments we have learned to shelter ourselves from. What I discovered is that fear is nothing but "chatter." It is made up of all the negative projections we have absorbed from everyone and everything around us through our lives. IT IS NOT REAL!

Remember: What is my proof & truth? What am I grateful for? What do I affirm? What is my intention?

Buying into someone else's fearful projection, about life, illness, health or healing, will only hinder your path. As my grandmother Cook used to say, "Half the stuff we worry about does not ever happen."

Remember: Use this page to doodle, draw or sketch.what you feel or dreamed.

I remember a relationship I was in where I suspected that my lover was going to leave me. I was convinced that I was not good enough for him. I unconsciously projected my childhood fear of abandonment onto my counterpart, and presto I chased him away and he left. I created havoc where it did not belong. I understand now that all of my beliefs were attachments, and illusions. Right here and now my life is great and, "I" am in charge of how I choose to think. Everything is perfectly fine. Yippee!

Remember: What is my proof & truth? What am I grateful for? What do I affirm? What is my intention?

*"The most courageous act is still to think for yourself. Aloud."~ **Coco Chanel***

When you work to heal your brokenness caused by the end of a relationship, you understand that your brokenness was but the symptom to the deeper and earlier root cause – childhood experience – and it was that which you needed to heal, otherwise you would be continuing to recreate it. You see, the past does not define who you are, this means, you can celebrate how you have become, WISE!

Remember: What is my proof & truth? What am I grateful for? What do I affirm? What is my intention?

Fear is the root cause behind unthinkable wars, ethnic cleansing, massacres and genocides on our planet. Fear is also the root cause behind domestic violence and all forms of assault and abuse within families and communities. When you make a decision if it coming from fear, STOP IT! What would your decision be if no fear were present? Yes, Grasshopper; there is your answer. *"Only Thing We Have to Fear Is Fear Itself" ~ Franklin D. Roosevelt First Inaugural Address*

Remember: Use this page to doodle, draw or sketch.what you feel or dreamed.

Fear is the evil driving force behind all pain and suffering. It can be bad or good. Choose wisely. It is so powerful it is also behind such extraordinary acts of bravery as the mother who lifted the car off of her child. The fear of losing her child filled her with super human power. This power is love. Fear is the opposite of love.

Remember: What is my proof & truth? What am I grateful for? What do I affirm? What is my intention?

"Fear knocked at the door. Love answered and no one was there." ~ **Wayne Dyer**

Remember: Use this page to doodle, draw or sketch.what you feel or dreamed.

Abandonment, chases relationships. Having experienced abandonment in our formative years, it is likely that later on in life we attract relationships in which we feel triggered and threatened that we will be rejected and abandoned again. These relationships are our mirrors, forcing us to face and heal our earlier traumatic memories. When we let go of the hurts of the past, we are no longer afraid, and we stand in our authentic power attracting the right relationship into our lives. Yes, you are worthy and deserving.

Remember: What is my proof & truth? What am I grateful for? What do I affirm? What is my intention?

*"Self-worth comes from one thing - thinking that you are worthy."~ **Wayne Dyer***

Remember: Use this page to doodle, draw or sketch.what you feel or dreamed.

Every person who shows up on your doorstep will mirror your wonderful characteristics as well as the flawed ones. Celebrate the former and work on the latter.

Remember: What is my proof & truth? What am I grateful for? What do I affirm? What is my intention?

*"Don't ever let someone tell you the value you don't have, in order to be in someone's life. That is often the value they feel you have, not that person." ~ **Shannon L. Alder***

Remember: Use this page to doodle, draw or sketch.what you feel or dreamed.

We settle into relationships that are unsatisfying, unhealthy, even dangerous, because we are afraid to be alone. Let us not rock the boat. It is safer to stay with what we know. Fear of the unknown is eclipsing our thinking. What about being with the *right person* who will add sunshine into your life? Make self-honoring choices. It is your turn to look up and see the sunshine. Love yourself and allow life to show you how worthy and deserving you are.

*"Love did not have to make sense. It did not have to be worthy. It did not have to be earned. It did not have to woo. It just simply was." ~ **Mary Balogh***

....

....

....

....

....

....

....

....

....

....

....

....

....

....

....

....

....

....

....

....

....

Remember: Use this page to doodle, draw or sketch.what you feel or dreamed.

Our inner child is creative, imaginative, adorable and innocent. Unfortunately, it is also the part in us that was hurt in childhood, and the wounds may still be bleeding. Until we heal this part, we are all children living in an adult body. Our inner child is unconsciously running our adult behaviors and reactions. What we experienced as children we have become. You are an adult now, take back your power and thrive. Last time I checked the adult is responsible for helping the child. You are the grown up and you get to decide how you want to think and live your life. You are still adorable and loving.

Remember: What is my proof & truth? What am I grateful for? What do I affirm? What is my intention?

You will find that after your inner child, or past experience, is healed, your adult self will experience the freedom you seek. Think of a beautiful rainbow with all its colors. The promise is this, " It will never rain that hard again."

Look at what upsets and causes you to react in a negative way. It is usually something carried into adulthood from the past. What ever you see let it go. Allow yourself to experience the freedom you desire to live. It's your turn to shine. As you look into the mirror notice; you are a shining star.

Assure the inner child that it will never be invalidated; give it what he/or she was deprived of, tell this precious being, I love you!

Remember: Use this page to doodle, draw or sketch.what you feel or dreamed.

You are not your old story, you are what you have now created, a new healthy one. What pretty story, pictures have you created?

....

....

....

....

....

....

....

....

....

....

....

....

....

....

....

....

....

....

....

....

....

....

....

....

Remember: What is my proof & truth? What am I grateful for? What do I affirm? What is my intention?

Children who suffer from the pain of abandonment want to be loved and approved of, and they continue to search for it their entire lives. "I am desperate for love," "I am not good enough," I am unworthy." Those of you who experienced some form of abandonment in childhood, extreme or subtle, it is important to learn to love yourself. You are worthy of love just by being born.

Remember: Use this page to doodle, draw or sketch.what you feel or dreamed.

Walk in grace, and life will not fail you. What are you grateful for? *If we learn to open our hearts, anyone, including the people who drive us crazy, can be our teacher. ~ Pema Chödrön*

We've all experienced being bombarded by unstoppable negative thoughts all day and night long. This negative chatter gets in the way of our healthy and creative thoughts, and opens the door to an avalanche of fearful beliefs, feelings and behaviors. STOP IT! They are not true. Right here and now you are perfectly fine. Let go of the attachment to what you think is wrong, take a deep breath and choose a healthy thought. *"Everything can be taken from a man but one thing: the last of human freedoms - to choose one's attitude in any given set of circumstances, to choose one's own way."* ~ **Viktor E. Frankl**

Remember: Use this page to doodle, draw or sketch.what you feel or dreamed.

"Do not dwell in the past, do not dream of the future, concentrate the mind on the present moment." ~ Buddha

Remember: What is my proof & truth? What am I grateful for? What do I affirm? What is my intention?

Fiction can turn into an attachment. The stronger the attachment the stronger the illusion. The stronger the illusion the stronger the attachment.

Remember: Use this page to doodle, draw or sketch.what you feel or dreamed.

Fiction is like a spider's web, attached ever so slightly perhaps, but still attached to life at all four corners. Often the attachment is scarcely perceptible. ~Virginia Woolf

Remember: What is my proof & truth? What am I grateful for? What do I affirm? What is my intention?

If you hear negative thoughts – listen and acknowledge its pain and fear, speak to it calmly and lovingly, and free yourself from the endless slavery of unhealed upset. The past you can never get back, stop bringing it up, move forward. Life is good! Your eyes and heart can choose what it wants to see and believe. Can you imagine right now the color yellow? Yes, it is bright and you can smile.

Remember: Use this page to doodle, draw or sketch.what you feel or dreamed.

"If I am walking with two other men, each of them will serve as my teacher. I will pick out the good points of the one and imitate them, and the bad points of the other and correct them in myself." ~ **Confucius**

Remember: What is my proof & truth? What am I grateful for? What do I affirm? What is my intention?

Fear. I tell my clients to stop, take a deep breath, and ask the deepest voice inside of them what they should do. I ask them to listen for the answer without judging, evaluating or negating it. Your truth will shine through and you will now make the right choice. We all have the answers within ourselves; all we have to do is listen.

Remember: Use this page to doodle, draw or sketch.what you feel or dreamed.

Feelings are trying to get your attention that something is wrong and they want you to do something about it. "*The best years of your life are the ones in which you decide your problems are your own. You do not blame them on your mother, the ecology, or the president. You realize that you control your own destiny.*" ~ *Albert Ellis*

It's time to take care of yourself! Animals go into a quiet corner and lick their wounds, nurturing themselves. Having realized that you are settling for a life or a relationship that is "less than" what you want or deserve, you may want to take a step back and search for the lesson you are being asked to face. Be kind to yourself.

Remember: Use this page to doodle, draw or sketch.what you feel or dreamed.

A projection is a disowned and unrecognized characteristic within ourselves that we attach to someone else. When we refuse to recognize a particular characteristic or behavior in ourselves, life will present us with a person who embodies that characteristic and behavior. Only when we take personal responsibility and change our perceptions will we change the world we live in. Here's the deal, projection can be good. When we are happy our world is happy, this is a good one!

We must recognize our projections before we can change our negative thoughts and beliefs. Like cobwebs hiding in the attic – you don't know they are there until you go up and look. As cobwebs will take over the attic if not cleaned out, so our negative thoughts and beliefs will take over our lives and make us miserable if we don't reframe them.

Remember: Use this page to doodle, draw or sketch.what you feel or dreamed.

Whether trying to solve relationship issues, weight loss, or any other issue, you'll discover that your belief systems are based on your past. The past has become your identity. STOP IT!

If you listen carefully, you will perceive how someone is seeing the world. You will perceive their past through a transparent present. What do they see when they look at you? What do you see when you look at yourself? What do "you" believe? Here's an idea; look in the mirror and tell yourself how great you are.

Relationships are fertile ground for old beliefs to sprout in, creating pain and havoc. But relationships are also the space in which to heal and change these old beliefs, and "test" them. Relationships can also mirror how healthy and happy you are.

Remember: What is my proof & truth? What am I grateful for? What do I affirm? What is my intention?

The future is an illusion. We have no idea what is going to happen. Most of the time, the here and now is perfectly fine. As my grandmother used to say: "Rochelle, not everything you worry about is going to happen." Indeed not everything we worry about ever happens, unless we make it happen. What do you believe?

....

....

....

....

....

....

....

....

....

....

....

....

....

....

....

....

....

....

....

....

....

....

Remember: Use this page to doodle, draw or sketch.what you feel or dreamed.

Life is much better when your glass is not half empty; it's over flowing!

Often we react to a situation as if it were a past experience and not the here and now. I used to be constantly afraid that a man I was in relationship with was going to leave me because "I'm not good enough." HA, I don't think so. Our experiences no matter what they are only make us into the magnificent people we are today.

"Everything has beauty, but not everyone sees it." ~ **Confucius**

Remember: What is my proof & truth? What am I grateful for? What do I affirm? What is my intention?

*Remember that throughout your life the greatest people on earth will pass. ~ **Michael Glock Ph.D.***

Remember: Use this page to doodle, draw or sketch.what you feel or dreamed.

Foremost, build a loving relationship with yourself then, you can be in relationship with another person.

Remember: What is my proof & truth? What am I grateful for? What do I affirm? What is my intention?

Life is one big projection. We project our belief systems onto everything and everyone. We are what we have been taught, some of our teachers were empowering and others disabling. Understanding this is key to a healthy personal and peaceful life.

Remember: Use this page to doodle, draw or sketch.what you feel or dreamed.

You no longer need anyone else to validate you for who you are. You know who you are. Fabulous!

Remember: What is my proof & truth? What am I grateful for? What do I affirm? What is my intention?

In relationships we project our beliefs onto the other person. In my office I often hear, "It's my way or the highway." But everything does not have to be just one way! What about being flexible and letting go of the way you think it ought to be, and listen to what your partner wants? What about asking yourself what you want? Are you being heard? Are your needs being met? It works both ways.

Remember: Use this page to doodle, draw or sketch. what you feel or dreamed.

We settle into an unhealthy and unhappy relationship because leaving it is too frightening, we'd be pitted against an unknown future that could be even worse. If we track this pattern back to an earlier time in our lives, we'll discover that somewhere in our formative years we experienced pain and trauma from which we concluded that we were unworthy and undeserving of a better life. That conclusion is ingrained in our subconscious and still calling the shots. But with inner child work and by identifying our projections it is possible to mend the wounds of the past, to recognize our worth, and find the strength of heart to move forward toward the life and relationship we seek. The sun will shine again in fact, in some places it is shinning right here and now!

Remember: What is my proof & truth? What am I grateful for? What do I affirm? What is my intention?

Our behaviors reflect our hidden wounds asking to be healed. *"Let us always meet each other with a smile, for the smile is the beginning of love."* ~ **Mother Teresa**

Remember: Use this page to doodle, draw or sketch.what you feel or dreamed.

If we want a more peaceful world, it's time to find the root causes of our own destructive behaviors toward others and ourselves. "Peace begins with me," goes the saying. *"I have decided to stick with love. Hate is too great a burden to bear."* ~ **Martin Luther King, Jr**

A peaceful life will follow a peaceful mind. Some will call this a state of enlightenment, nirvana, or satori, to name a few options. To reach this state we must first do the psychological work: feel, understand, reframe, and change our thinking. As the saying goes: we become enlightened by shedding light on the darkness.

Remember: Use this page to doodle, draw or sketch.what you feel or dreamed.

With a peaceful and centered state of mind, devoid of self-criticism and rooted in your authentic power, it will be easier for you to attract the life and relationship you desire.

Remember: What is my proof & truth? What am I grateful for? What do I affirm? What is my intention?

Your addictive and destructive behaviors are here to call you to change. They are the logs to be burned in the fire of your emotional healing and spiritual transformation. As you work on resolving your issues, watch those logs being burned to ashes and taken into the upper realms to be transmuted into love, peace and harmony.

Remember: Use this page to doodle, draw or sketch.what you feel or dreamed.

"The psychic task which a person can and must set for himself is not to feel secure, but to be able to tolerate insecurity." ~ Erich Fromm

Remember: What is my proof & truth? What am I grateful for? What do I affirm? What is my intention?

You do not need anyone in order to be whole – you are already whole.

Make yourself whole first. Expressions such as "she is my better half" romanticize an illusion, for a relationship between two "halves" is doomed to fail. When you're whole in yourself and rest in that knowing, you will no longer chase someone else to fill in the lack you feel inside.

Remember: What is my proof & truth? What am I grateful for? What do I affirm? What is my intention?

"Happiness depends upon ourselves." ~ Aristotle

I think it's important to really love yourself. You always have you! *"We're born alone, we live alone, we die alone. Only through our love and friendship can we create the illusion for the moment that we're not alone."* ~ **Orson Welles**

·······

Remember: What is my proof & truth? What am I grateful for? What do I affirm? What is my intention?

*"You can search throughout the entire universe for someone who is more deserving of your love and affection than you are yourself, and that person is not to be found anywhere. You yourself, as much as anybody in the entire universe deserve your love and affection." ~ **Buddha***

....

....

....

....

....

....

....

....

....

....

....

....

....

....

....

....

....

....

....

....

....

....

....

Remember: Use this page to doodle, draw or sketch.what you feel or dreamed.

I remember the heartache of constantly searching outside myself for love. If someone loved me that meant I was okay because they validated me. If the person did not love me, that was it. I would march myself right back into the trash can of pain and sorrow. I had to learn how to reframe my perspective and make peace with my story so that I could move forward. Well, I have. Things look different now; I no longer become upset over too much of anything. I know that I will always have myself, approve of myself and make what ever is happening ok. Most of the time my here and now is great, the fictitious world I used to live in is gone! Life is good and I can fly with my friend, the seagull, free, above the ocean and allow the currents to take me where I need to go.

Remember: What is my proof & truth? What am I grateful for? What do I affirm? What is my intention?

When a therapist asked me: "What would happen if you sat in your chair and allowed someone to come to you," I thought she was speaking Chinese! Because I believed that no one would ever come to me. When you learn to love yourself guess what? It happens, they come!

Remember: Use this page to doodle, draw or sketch.what you feel or dreamed.

The only person you can "get back" is you, because the truth is that you never lost it, you just forgot.

Remember: What is my proof & truth? What am I grateful for? What do I affirm? What is my intention?

Those who judge others are those who judge themselves.

Remember: Use this page to doodle, draw or sketch.what you feel or dreamed.

Know one has the right to judge another person. They are only living the curriculum they were summoned to live, show compassion for their journey. This includes your own.

....

....

....

....

....

....

....

....

....

....

....

....

....

....

....

....

....

....

....

....

....

Remember: What is my proof & truth? What am I grateful for? What do I affirm? What is my intention?

Dear Inner Child, You do not need anyone to make you feel safe or loved – because you have me.

Remember: Use this page to doodle, draw or sketch.what you feel or dreamed.

"Life can only be understood backwards; but it must be lived forwards." ~ **Soren Kierkegaard**

Remember: What is my proof & truth? What am I grateful for? What do I affirm? What is my intention?

Your outer reality is a reflection of your inner reality. What are your beliefs that play out in your life?

....

....

....

....

....

....

....

....

....

....

....

....

....

....

....

....

....

....

....

....

....

Remember: Use this page to doodle, draw or sketch.what you feel or dreamed.

When you are upset and feel unworthy and undeserving, ask yourself, is it really so? Am I really unworthy and undeserving? Am I stupid, like I have been told I am, or has someone else been projecting onto me? How many of my beliefs are actually my own? How many are my parents' or my teachers' or have come from the culture at large? How have I been infected with the Story Book Syndrome? The answer is NO. The story you were taught belongs to somebody else. What is your, "real" story? Love, compassion, acceptance, lack of judgment towards yourself and others, and happiness! What matters is what "you" think not what, "they" think.

....

....

....

....

....

....

....

....

....

....

....

....

....

....

....

....

....

....

....

Remember: What is my proof & truth? What am I grateful for? What do I affirm? What is my intention?

"We love life, not because we are used to living but because we are used to loving."
~ Friedrich Nietzsche

Remember: Use this page to doodle, draw or sketch.what you feel or dreamed.

Find a mantra that empowers you, and when in doubt, when you forget who you are, repeat it to yourself. Hold on tight to it until you remember who you are, until you realize that you are the perfect you!

Remember: What is my proof & truth? What am I grateful for? What do I affirm? What is my intention?

What we learn in a traumatic childhood becomes our identity, until we unlearn it – until we heal it. What we learned, we can unlearn.

"The outward work will never be puny if the inward work is great." ~ *Meister Eckhart*

Remember: What is my proof & truth? What am I grateful for? What do I affirm? What is my intention?

Life often brings us into situations that force us to go beyond our perceived limitations.

To be in a healthy relationship we must be in healthy relationship with ourselves. We all have a curriculum to learn – for some, the lessons are more difficult that for others. Hardship is an opportunity to learn our lessons. We can take what we learn and thrive.

Remember: What is my proof & truth? What am I grateful for? What do I affirm? What is my intention?

Living on planet Earth can be seen as a training camp: our souls came into this life with the purpose of becoming more whole.

Remember: Use this page to doodle, draw or sketch.what you feel or dreamed.

"All journeys have secret destinations of which the traveler is unaware." ~ **Martin Buber**

Remember: What is my proof & truth? What am I grateful for? What do I affirm? What is my intention?

In the process of dealing with our obstacles and antagonists, we can learn unconditional-love, honesty, forgiveness, compassion and happiness – and so, become more whole.

Remember: Use this page to doodle, draw or sketch.what you feel or dreamed.

If we find ourselves behaving in ways that are disturbing to us or to our surroundings, we better listen carefully. This behavior is an indication that something is wrong on a deeper level. We are unconsciously playing out our unresolved childhood traumas and wounds. Identifying our destructive behaviors, understanding and healing their root causes, will lead us on our journey toward the life we so wish for.

Remember: What is my proof & truth? What am I grateful for? What do I affirm? What is my intention?

Fighting against our reality, not accepting WHAT IS, is like going to ski in the winter in a bathing suit. *"Acceptance doesn't mean resignation; it means understanding that something is what it is and that there's got to be a way through it."* ~ **Michael J. Fox**

Remember: Use this page to doodle, draw or sketch.what you feel or dreamed.

"To love oneself is the beginning of a life-long romance." ~ *Oscar* **Wilde**

Remember: What is my proof & truth? What am I grateful for? What do I affirm? What is my intention?

Once we accept our situation, the stuck, lost energy is released to our disposal. We can breathe now. It is said, "The truth shall set you free."

Remember: Use this page to doodle, draw or sketch.what you feel or dreamed.

"To be beautiful means to be yourself. You don't need to be accepted by others. You need to accept yourself." **~Thich Nhat Hanh**

Remember: What is my proof & truth? What am I grateful for? What do I affirm? What is my intention?

We must learn to sit in the discomfort of our feelings without numbing or distracting ourselves. We must learn to accept how we feel ok.

Remember: Use this page to doodle, draw or sketch.what you feel or dreamed.

When we finally recognize and accept that we are in the "belly of the whale," there is nothing else to do but feel the pain and accept our entire life story – as is – with its agony – and its glory – and ourselves as the heroes and heroines on a journey of transformation.

Acceptance does not mean that we agree with or submit ourselves to an abusive or painful relationship; it means that we recognize what is going on, find a safe space to express our hurt, and then, mindfully and sensibly, deal with and heal the situation. Accept what ever situation you are in, stop fighting so hard and trust that your life will unfold and you will be ok.

Remember: What is my proof & truth? What am I grateful for? What do I affirm? What is my intention?

"The possible ranks higher than the actual." ~ **Martin Heidegger**

Life is good, instead of looking at the glass half empty; see how full it is. What are you grateful for?

Remember: What is my proof & truth? What am I grateful for? What do I affirm? What is my intention?

It is crucial to remember that every unbearable, upsetting, shameful situation can be seen as a tragedy, or as a lesson to tackle, heal, and evolve. It is your choice.

Remember: Use this page to doodle, draw or sketch.what you feel or dreamed.

When you finally accept that your life is far from being what you wish it were and what you feel it could be, it is time to find out what YOU are doing that is affecting YOU. Remember, again, that your outer world is a reflection of your inner world.

"I prefer to be true to myself, even at the hazard of incurring the ridicule of others, rather than to be false, and to incur my own abhorrence." ~ **Frederick Douglass**

Remember: Use this page to doodle, draw or sketch.what you feel or dreamed.

Stop, take a breath, look at the situation, examine your own behaviors and belief systems, accept the whole scenario, and act pro-actively – change your thoughts – change your attitude.

Remember: What is my proof & truth? What am I grateful for? What do I affirm? What is my intention?

So we have an irrational thought like "Unless I change, I will never have another lover," or "I'll lose all my money," or "my girlfriend is going to leave me"... so what do I do? Use your finger and press DELETE! A space has just opened. If you don't place a healthy thought in this empty space, you risk letting another old, irrational thoughts slip right in – Your glass is not empty!

Remember: Use this page to doodle, draw or sketch.what you feel or dreamed.

The more you practice changing your thoughts on a regular basis, the easier and faster the process will become.

Remember: What is my proof & truth? What am I grateful for? What do I affirm? What is my intention?

Acceptance is the turning point. The turning point means, first and foremost, turning inward. It means turning inward to "Know Thyself" as Socrates has taught us.

Remember: Use this page to doodle, draw or sketch.what you feel or dreamed.

*"Science is organized knowledge. Wisdom is organized life." ~ **Immanuel Kant***

Remember: What is my proof & truth? What am I grateful for? What do I affirm? What is my intention?

When we understand our life's story, some of which has been hidden in the subconscious mind, we become acquainted with more of our strengths, and talents too. This is how we turn toward ourselves! We learn to better love ourselves, pay attention to our needs, and find healthy ways to fulfill them.

Remember: Use this page to doodle, draw or sketch.what you feel or dreamed.

Turning inward will change your relationship with yourself, and in response your relationships in the outside world will change as well.

"The privilege of a lifetime is to become who you truly are." ~ **C.G. Jung**

Remember: Use this page to doodle, draw or sketch.what you feel or dreamed.

In each moment, with every unpleasant or irrational thought, we have a choice – a turning point – to go tumbling down with our thinking, or to change it and see our state of mind and life change as well. The turning point is a point in time as much as it is a process. It happens once, and then it happens again and again. It's an exciting journey of adventure and discovery that requires daily mindful maintenance. The payoff is huge!

Remember: What is my proof & truth? What am I grateful for? What do I affirm? What is my intention?

It Matters What You Think, Not What "They" Think

If something in your relationship is upsetting you, look carefully into your own mirror. That mirror, your relationship, is trying to teach you what you are suffering from. What is really upsetting you? Take your index finger and point it towards yourself, yes, yourself, not them!

Remember: What is my proof & truth? What am I grateful for? What do I affirm? What is my intention?

No one can disturb your peace unless you allow them to. ~ **Dr. Ronald Hulnick**

I am upset because "I." Not because of "them." That's the key to healing, pointing the finger outward, which may take the heat off you, but perpetuates the vicious cycle of pain and blame. As my mother used to tell me and still does: *"People who live in glass houses shouldn't throw stones."*

Remember: What is my proof & truth? What am I grateful for? What do I affirm? What is my intention?

"There is no coming to consciousness without pain. People will do anything, no matter how absurd, in order to avoid facing their own Soul. One does not become enlightened by imagining figures of light, but by making the darkness conscious." ~ **C.G. Jung**

Remember: Use this page to doodle, draw or sketch.what you feel or dreamed.

"The greatest tragedy of the family is the unlived lives of the parents." ~ C.G. Jung

Remember: What is my proof & truth? What am I grateful for? What do I affirm? What is my intention?

Each time we are triggered is an opportunity to look at ourselves and inquire within why are we so upset. If the answer is steeped in honesty, so is the potential for recovery and growth.

Learn to distinguish between the world views and values you were indoctrinated into and obligated to live by, and your own discoveries, insights and personal choices. Practice being true to yourself!

"What is not brought to consciousness, comes to us as fate."

Remember: What is my proof & truth? What am I grateful for? What do I affirm? What is my intention?

"The pendulum of the mind oscillates between sense and nonsense, not between right and wrong." ~ C.G. Jung

Remember: Use this page to doodle, draw or sketch.what you feel or dreamed.

No matter what your past was like you are worthy and deserving.

Try to have the understanding that whatever is happening in your relationship right here and now is perfect. Even when it is imperfect, it is perfect.

Remember: Use this page to doodle, draw or sketch.what you feel or dreamed.

Choose to change the way you think, first and foremost about yourself, and let go of all the "do's" and the "don'ts" that were planted and imprinted into you.

Remember: What is my proof & truth? What am I grateful for? What do I affirm? What is my intention?

So dare to discard all that you have been taught from the moment you were born until now that no longer serves you, and accept the present moment without judgment.

"All that we see or seem, is but a dream within a dream." ~Edgar Allan Poe

Remember: What is my proof & truth? What am I grateful for? What do I affirm? What is my intention?

Find the courage to rise above preconceived notions and ideas of what you should be. Become present and look at life through a new set of eyes. There is no need to dwell on the past once you have understood, cleared and healed it. There is no need to speculate about the future; often what is in store for us is way better than our wildest imaginations. Treasure the journey – be in the NOW – it will change your life and create a great future.

Remember: Use this page to doodle, draw or sketch.what you feel or dreamed.

You are a soul having a human experience. Often the experience can be difficult. It should not be judged as wrong. Opting to see that this is true, you begin to view life differently. You understand that taking a human birth is like entering a school, and you are willing to participate fully and learn all the lessons.

You recognize your gifts of compassion and insight and you generously share them with the one you love.

....

....

....

....

....

....

....

....

....

....

....

....

....

....

....

....

....

....

....

....

....

....

....

Remember: Use this page to doodle, draw or sketch.what you feel or dreamed.

Instead of living your life as a half-empty-glass, trust that your glass is overflowing with goodness and wisdom.

No one is better than anyone else; we are just different, with different crosses to bear.

Remember: Use this page to doodle, draw or sketch.what you feel or dreamed.

Taking back your power means that you are no longer a victim, and you don't behave unconsciously and reactively. Instead, you are mindful and live in the awareness that your relationships are mirrors that reflect back to you who you are: what inside you is gracious and light, and what you still need to accept and to heal. So give thanks to the mirror, and in so doing you will also be giving thanks to yourself.

Remember: What is my proof & truth? What am I grateful for? What do I affirm? What is my intention?

Accepting that we have a problem is the most important and most difficult step on the healing journey. It is almost impossible to accept such challenging situations as bankruptcy or one's teenage child's addiction to a heavy drug, or the infidelity of a spouse. It is equally difficult to accept our own inner "enemies" such as envy, rage or self-loathing. But when we find ourselves swallowed into the "Belly of the Whale" by any such ordeals, there is no other way but to accept our reality and continue our restoration without losing energy on resentment and debate. *"A ruffled mind makes a restless pillow."* ~*Charlotte Brontë* Acceptance leads to change, and change leads to freedom.

Remember: Use this page to doodle, draw or sketch.what you feel or dreamed.

Everything can be taken from a man but one thing: the last of the human freedoms – to choose one's attitude in any given set of circumstances, to choose one's own way.

"When we are no longer able to change a situation – we are challenged to change ourselves." ~ Dr. Viktor Frankl

....

....

....

....

....

....

....

....

....

....

....

....

....

....

....

....

....

....

....

....

....

....

....

Remember: Use this page to doodle, draw or sketch.what you feel or dreamed.

"The Breeze of Grace Is Always Blowing; Set Your Sail to Catch That Breeze."
~ Ramakrishna Paramahansa

Remember: What is my proof & truth? What am I grateful for? What do I affirm? What is my intention?

"Intention" is one of the most powerful words in the universe!

....

....

....

....

....

....

....

....

....

....

....

....

....

....

....

....

....

....

....

....

....

....

Remember: Use this page to doodle, draw or sketch.what you feel or dreamed.

The most essential intention you can make, and one that will enliven and empower every step you take, is the intention to love yourself and your life, always, whether the intentions you'll be setting materialize or not.

Remember: What is my proof & truth? What am I grateful for? What do I affirm? What is my intention?

I ask for the alignment of heaven and earth to see me through.

"Learning lessons is a little like reaching maturity. You're not suddenly more happy, wealthy, or powerful, but you understand the world around you better, and you're at peace with yourself. Learning life's lessons is not about making your life perfect, but about seeing life as it was meant to be." ~ Elisabeth Kubler-Ross

Remember: What is my proof & truth? What am I grateful for? What do I affirm? What is my intention?

No matter what happens, I accept what comes my way.

An intention does not have to be set in stone. It is not a commitment. It can be altered or terminated.

Intention can start with a whisper deep inside, with an impulse, a need, or a dream in the night.

Remember: Use this page to doodle, draw or sketch.what you feel or dreamed.

It is important to create intentions that come from *your* needs, your heart, not intentions you are forced to make.

*"A dream which is not interpreted is like a letter which is not read." ~**The Talmud***

"Changing the present, into ....."

Instructions:

Take the plunge into the glorious garden you are planting. Sow the seeds of new thoughts in order to create positive conditions in your future life. Remember ... "Your words are the house in which you live." You do not have to list 100 hundred, all at once, take your time, do some today some tomorrow. Some people write their accomplishments down every day before they go to sleep. Take your time, you can do it!

Examples:

I forgive myself for the misbelief that... I am not a good person, I am what I was told as a child, stupid. THIS IS NOT TRUE!

I forgive myself for the misbelief that... I can hold onto a good job and that I have no "stay power." THIS IS NOT TRUE!

I forgive myself for the misbelief that... everyone is going to leave me because I'm damaged goods. I'm not good enough, "THIS IS NOT TRUE, HOGWASH!

NOW WRITE YOUR OWN...

1. I forgive myself for the misbelief that, ...

....

2. I forgive myself for the misbelief that, ...

....

3. I forgive myself for the misbelief that, ...

....

4. I forgive myself for the misbelief that,

5. I forgive myself for the misbelief that,

6. I forgive myself for the misbelief that,

7. I forgive myself for the misbelief that,

8. I forgive myself for the misbelief that,

9. I forgive myself for the misbelief that,

10. I forgive myself for the misbelief that,

11. I forgive myself for the misbelief that,

12. I forgive myself for the misbelief that,

13. I forgive myself for the misbelief that,

14. I forgive myself for the misbelief that,

15. I forgive myself for the misbelief that,

16. I forgive myself for the misbelief that,

17. I forgive myself for the misbelief that,

18. I forgive myself for the misbelief that,

19. I forgive myself for the misbelief that,

20. I forgive myself for the misbelief that,

21. I forgive myself for the misbelief that,

22. I forgive myself for the misbelief that,

23. I forgive myself for the misbelief that,

24. I forgive myself for the misbelief that,

25. I forgive myself for the misbelief that,

26. I forgive myself for the misbelief that,

27. I forgive myself for the misbelief that,

28. I forgive myself for the misbelief that,

29. I forgive myself for the misbelief that,

30. I forgive myself for the misbelief that,

31. I forgive myself for the misbelief that,

32. I forgive myself for the misbelief that,

33. I forgive myself for the misbelief that,

34. I forgive myself for the misbelief that,

35. I forgive myself for the misbelief that,

36. I forgive myself for the misbelief that,

37. I forgive myself for the misbelief that,

38. I forgive myself for the misbelief that,

39. I forgive myself for the misbelief that,

40. I forgive myself for the misbelief that,

41. I forgive myself for the misbelief that,

42. I forgive myself for the misbelief that,

43. I forgive myself for the misbelief that,

44. I forgive myself for the misbelief that,

45. I forgive myself for the misbelief that,

46. I forgive myself for the misbelief that,

47. I forgive myself for the misbelief that,

48. I forgive myself for the misbelief that,

49. I forgive myself for the misbelief that,

50. I forgive myself for the misbelief that,

51. I forgive myself for the misbelief that,

52. I forgive myself for the misbelief that,

53. I forgive myself for the misbelief that,

54. I forgive myself for the misbelief that,

55. I forgive myself for the misbelief that,

56. I forgive myself for the misbelief that,

57. I forgive myself for the misbelief that,

58. I forgive myself for the misbelief that,

59. I forgive myself for the misbelief that,

60. I forgive myself for the misbelief that,

61. I forgive myself for the misbelief that,

62. I forgive myself for the misbelief that,

63. I forgive myself for the misbelief that,

64. I forgive myself for the misbelief that,

65. I forgive myself for the misbelief that,

66. I forgive myself for the misbelief that,

67. I forgive myself for the misbelief that,

68. I forgive myself for the misbelief that,

69. I forgive myself for the misbelief that,

70. I forgive myself for the misbelief that,

71. I forgive myself for the misbelief that,

72. I forgive myself for the misbelief that,

73. I forgive myself for the misbelief that,

74. I forgive myself for the misbelief that,

75. I forgive myself for the misbelief that,

76. I forgive myself for the misbelief that,

77. I forgive myself for the misbelief that,

78. I forgive myself for the misbelief that,

79. I forgive myself for the misbelief that,

80. I forgive myself for the misbelief that,

81. I forgive myself for the misbelief that,

82. I forgive myself for the misbelief that,

83. I forgive myself for the misbelief that,

84. I forgive myself for the misbelief that,

85. I forgive myself for the misbelief that,

86. I forgive myself for the misbelief that,

87. I forgive myself for the misbelief that,

88. I forgive myself for the misbelief that,

89. I forgive myself for the misbelief that,

90. I forgive myself for the misbelief that,

91. I forgive myself for the misbelief that,

92. I forgive myself for the misbelief that,

93. I forgive myself for the misbelief that,

94. I forgive myself for the misbelief that,

95. I forgive myself for the misbelief that,

96. I forgive myself for the misbelief that,

97. I forgive myself for the misbelief that,

98. I forgive myself for the misbelief that,

99. I forgive myself for the misbelief that,

100. I forgive myself for the misbelief that,

Examples:

The truth is... I am a great person, people like me and I am far from stupid! I am an intelligent person that people want to learn from! I am a teacher! My father was only projecting his inadequacies on to me. These are his issue's not mine, I no longer believe them because I know they are not true! I am smart and as quick as a whip!

The truth is... I can hold down any job I please. I know that if I really want to do something I will! My parents gave me everything in the world, including a trust fund, because they were poor when they were young. I want to get out in the world and make my own money. I do not have to rely on someone because I can take care of myself because I want to. I have a lot of stay power! I do not quit because I do not have to work, I am focused, strong and I will prevail!

The truth is... I am good enough, I know how to love and how I want to be treated because I have experienced the opposite. I love me and someone out there would be lucky to be in my life. I have a lot to give. I am a good person!

1. The truth is, ...

....

....

2. The truth is, ...

....

....

3. The truth is, ...

....

....

4. The truth is, ...

....

....

5. The truth is, ...

....

....

6. The truth is, ...

....

....

7. The truth is,

8. The truth is,

9. The truth is,

10. The truth is,

11. The truth is,

12. The truth is,

13. The truth is,

14. The truth is, ...

....

....

....

15. The truth is, ...

....

....

....

16. The truth is, ...

....

....

....

17. The truth is, ...

....

....

....

18. The truth is, ...

....

....

....

19. The truth is, ...

....

....

....

20. The truth is, ...

....

....

....

21. The truth is,

22. The truth is,

23. The truth is,

24. The truth is,

25. The truth is,

26. The truth is,

27. The truth is,

28. The truth is, ...

....

....

29. The truth is, ...

....

....

30. The truth is, ...

....

....

31. The truth is, ...

....

....

32. The truth is, ...

....

....

33. The truth is, ...

....

....

34. The truth is, ...

....

....

35. The truth is,

36. The truth is,

37. The truth is,

38. The truth is,

39. The truth is,

40. The truth is,

41. The truth is,

42. The truth is,

43. The truth is,

44. The truth is,

45. The truth is,

46. The truth is,

47. The truth is,

48. The truth is,

49. The truth is,

50. The truth is,

51. The truth is,

52. The truth is,

53. The truth is,

54. The truth is,

55. The truth is,

56. The truth is,

57. The truth is,

58. The truth is,

59. The truth is,

60. The truth is,

61. The truth is,

62. The truth is,

63. The truth is,

64. The truth is,

65. The truth is,

66. The truth is,

67. The truth is,

68. The truth is,

69. The truth is,

70. The truth is,

71. The truth is,

72. The truth is,

73. The truth is,

74. The truth is,

75. The truth is,

76. The truth is,

77. The truth is,

78. The truth is,

79. The truth is,

80. The truth is,

81. The truth is,

82. The truth is,

83. The truth is,

84. The truth is, ...
....
....

85. The truth is, ...
....
....

86. The truth is, ...
....
....

87. The truth is, ...
....
....

88. The truth is, ...
....
....

89. The truth is, ...
....
....

90. The truth is, ...
....
....

91. The truth is,

91. The truth is,

92. The truth is,

93. The truth is,

94. The truth is,

95. The truth is,

96. The truth is,

97. The truth is,

98. The truth is,

99. The truth is,

100. The truth is,

Examples:

1. "I am" grateful for ....

2. "I am" grateful for ....

3. "I am" grateful for ....

4. "I am" grateful for ....

5. "I am" grateful for ....

6. "I am" grateful for ....

7. "I am" grateful for ....

8. "I am" grateful for ....

9. "I am" grateful for ....

10. "I am" grateful for ....

11. "I am" grateful for ....

12. "I am" grateful for ....

13. "I am" grateful for ....

14. "I am" grateful for ....

....

15. "I am" grateful for ....

....

16. "I am" grateful for ....

....

17. "I am" grateful for ....

....

18. "I am" grateful for ....

....

19. "I am" grateful for ....

....

20. "I am" grateful for ....

....

21. "I am" grateful for ....

....

22. "I am" grateful for ....

....

23. "I am" grateful for ....

....

24. "I am" grateful for ....

....

25. "I am" grateful for ....

....

26. "I am" grateful for ....

....

27. "I am" grateful for ....

....

28. "I am" grateful for ....

29. "I am" grateful for ....

30. "I am" grateful for ....

31. "I am" grateful for ....

32. "I am" grateful for ....

33. "I am" grateful for ....

34. "I am" grateful for ....

35. "I am" grateful for ....

36. "I am" grateful for ....

37. "I am" grateful for ....

38. "I am" grateful for ....

39. "I am" grateful for ....

40. "I am" grateful for ....

41. "I am" grateful for ....

42. "I am" grateful for ....

....

43. "I am" grateful for ....

....

44. "I am" grateful for ....

....

45. "I am" grateful for ....

....

46. "I am" grateful for ....

....

47. "I am" grateful for ....

....

48. "I am" grateful for ....

....

49. "I am" grateful for ....

....

50. "I am" grateful for ....

....

51. "I am" grateful for ....

....

52. "I am" grateful for ....

....

53. "I am" grateful for ....

....

54. "I am" grateful for ....

....

55. "I am" grateful for ....

....

56. "I am" grateful for

57. "I am" grateful for

58. "I am" grateful for

59. "I am" grateful for

60. "I am" grateful for

61. "I am" grateful for

62. "I am" grateful for

63. "I am" grateful for

64. "I am" grateful for

65. "I am" grateful for

66. "I am" grateful for

67. "I am" grateful for

68. "I am" grateful for

69. "I am" grateful for

70. "I am" grateful for

....

71. "I am" grateful for

....

72. "I am" grateful for

....

73. "I am" grateful for

....

74. "I am" grateful for

....

75. "I am" grateful for

....

76. "I am" grateful for

....

77. "I am" grateful for

....

78. "I am" grateful for

....

79. "I am" grateful for

....

80. "I am" grateful for

....

81. "I am" grateful for

....

82. "I am" grateful for

....

83. "I am" grateful for

....

84. "I am" grateful for

85. "I am" grateful for

86. "I am" grateful for

87. "I am" grateful for

88. "I am" grateful for

89. "I am" grateful for

90. "I am" grateful for

91. "I am" grateful for

92. "I am" grateful for

93. "I am" grateful for

94. "I am" grateful for

95. "I am" grateful for

96. "I am" grateful for

97. "I am" grateful for

98. "I am" grateful for ....

....

99. "I am" grateful for ....

....

100. "I am" grateful for ....

....

Afterword:

A longing to wander tears my heart when I hear trees rustling in the wind.

For me, trees have always been the most penetrating preachers. I revere them when they live in tribes and families, in forests and groves. And even more I revere them when they stand-alone. They are like lonely persons. Not like hermits who have stolen away out of some weakness, but like great, solitary men, like Beethoven and Nietzsche. In their highest boughs the world rustles, their roots rest in infinity; but they do not lose themselves there, they struggle with all the force of their lives for one thing only: to fulfill themselves according to their own laws, to build up their own form, to represent themselves. Nothing is holier; nothing is more exemplary than a beautiful, strong tree. When a tree is cut down and reveals its naked death-wound to the sun, one can read its whole history in the luminous, inscribed disk of its trunk: in the rings of its years, its scars, all the struggle, all the suffering, all the sickness, all the happiness and prosperity stand truly written, the narrow years and the luxurious years, the attacks withstood, the storms endured. And every young farmboy knows that the hardest and noblest wood has the narrowest rings, that high on the mountains and in continuing danger the most indestructible, the strongest, the ideal trees grow.

Trees are sanctuaries. Whoever knows how to speak to them, whoever knows how to listen to them, can learn the truth. They do not preach learning and precepts, they preach, undeterred by particulars, the ancient law of life.

A tree says: A kernel is hidden in me, a spark, a thought; I am life from eternal life. The attempt and the risk that the eternal mother took with me is unique, unique the form and veins of my skin, unique the smallest play of leaves in my branches and the smallest scar on my bark. I was made to form and reveal the eternal in my smallest special detail.

A tree says: My strength is trust. I know nothing about my fathers; I know nothing about the thousand children that every year spring out of me. I live out the secret of my seed to the very end, and I care for nothing else. I trust that God is in me. I trust that my labor is holy. Out of this trust I live.

When we are stricken and cannot bear our lives any longer, then a tree has something to say to us: Be still! Be still! Look at me! Life is not easy, life is not difficult. Those are childish thoughts. Let God speak within you, and your thoughts will grow silent. You are anxious because your path leads away from mother and home. But every step and every day lead you back again to the mother. Home is neither here nor there. Home is within you, or home is nowhere at all.

A longing to wander tears my heart when I hear trees rustling in the wind at evening. If one listens to them silently for a long time, this longing reveals its kernel, its meaning. It is not so much a matter of escaping from one's suffering, though it may seem to be so. It is a longing for home, for a memory of the mother, for new metaphors for life. It leads home. Every path leads homeward, every step is birth, every step is death, every grave is mother.

So the tree rustles in the evening, when we stand uneasy before our own childish thoughts: Trees have long thoughts, long-breathing and restful, just as they have longer lives than ours. They are wiser than we are, as long as we do not listen to them. But when we have learned how to listen to trees, then the brevity and the quickness and the childlike hastiness of our thoughts achieve an incomparable joy. Whoever has learned how to listen to trees no longer wants to be a tree. He wants to be nothing except what he is. That is home. That is happiness."

Hermann Hesse, Bäume. Betrachtungen und Gedichte

Connect

With Rochelle L. Cook MA., ChT.

Since 2008, Rochelle L. Cook has introduced The Soul's Coaching Programs to thousands of people throughout the world. Visit her **online and become a member of the tribe** www. thesoulscoach.com

- ◆ Learn more about The Soul's Coaching Programs

- ◆ Become a member and listen and watch audio and video clips of Rochelle speaking and coaching

- ◆ Find out about weekend and scheduled workshop retreats

- ◆ Schedule a session with Rochelle

- ◆ Visit Rochelle on Facebook: rochelle.cook.587

- ◆ Visit Rochelle on LinkedIn: www.linkedin.com/in/thesoulscoach

- ◆ Visit Rochelle on Twitter: rochellelcook

- ◆ Visit Rochelle on Google+: https://plus.google.com/+RochelleLCook/

- ◆ Visit Rochelle on the Blog: www.thesoulscoach.com

- ◆ Visit Rochelle for Clinical ypnotherapy: www.rochellelcook.com

Change and shifts will always be a part of your life. Follow me and become a member of our growing tribe.

Nameste

Remember that with sharp tools the job is half finished. ~ **Erenst Glock**

Remember: What is my proof & truth? What am I grateful for? What do I affirm? What is my intention?

Made in the USA
Monee, IL
09 January 2021